W9-ARF-533

98.3

The Boeing Everett facility is the largest building in the world by volume. Its footprint covers 98.3 acres (39.9 hectares).

IN PLANE VIEW
A PICTORIAL TOUR OF THE **BOEING EVERETT FACTORY**

FIRST EDITION

CONTENTS

Since the late 1960s, people from every continent on the globe have toured the Boeing factory in Everett, Wash. First to see the massive 747 jumbo jet being assembled, then through the years the 767, the digitally designed 777 and the 787 Dreamliner – the airplane that ushered in a new era of flight. In this book, you'll find a brief history of the factory and facts about these amazing flying machines. Most of all you'll find compelling images of Boeing airplanes from factory floor to flight – airplanes that would not exist without the hard work and dedication of the men and women of Boeing who turn dreams of flight into reality on a daily basis.

FROM DREAMS TO REALITY

The Boeing Everett factory

It is the biggest building on earth by volume – the Boeing facility in Everett, Wash., has a footprint that covers 98.3 acres (39.95 hectares). That's 4.3 million square feet (more than 399,000 square meters), enough space for 911 basketball courts. This is where the 747, 767, 777 and 787 Dreamliner are assembled, painted, tested and ultimately delivered to customers. But Boeing was building airplanes in Everett long before the jumbo jet and the 787 Dreamliner. The beginning was small – the first factory was less than 32,000 square feet (2,973 square meters).

Small, but powerful beginnings

It all started in 1943 when Boeing built branch plants throughout Washington's Puget Sound area to support the buildup for World War II. In addition to building a plant in Everett, airplane facilities were established in Aberdeen, Bellingham, Chehalis and Tacoma. Work began at the North Everett plant Oct. 11, 1943 – Boeing Branch Plant 682 built radio compartments and bulkheads for the B-17 and then converted to B-29 pressure bulkhead work in 1944. The last delivery was made Sept. 5, 1945.

From "The Incredibles" to the dreamers

Then, during the late 1960s, some 50,000 Boeing people called "The Incredibles" – construction workers, mechanics, engineers, secretaries and administrators – made aviation history by building the 747 in less than 16 months. The world's first jumbo jet airplane required construction of the original factory, completed in 1968. The facility was expanded in 1980 for the 767 assembly line and again in the early 1990s for the 777. Each time the factory was expanded, it retained the title of world's largest building by volume. Overall, four new buildings were added; one had multiple nonassembly uses over the years – such as testing the 777 moving line. In May 2007, that building became the location of the final assembly line for the revolutionary new 787 Dreamliner.

Building by the numbers – millions of parts

Nearly all the parts and components of the airplanes that Boeing designs and assembles are manufactured elsewhere. A worldwide network of suppliers produces everything from brakes and fuselage panels to passenger call buttons. General Electric, Pratt & Whitney, and Rolls-Royce make the engines – the most expensive part on an airplane. Several suppliers within Boeing build interiors, electrical systems and electronics. It can take more than a year from the time a customer places an order until the airplane is ready for delivery. About half that time is needed to get the parts – the 787 has 2.3 million parts and the 767 has approximately 3 million – which are sent to the Everett factory by truck, ship, rail and jet.

High-efficiency assemblies

The Boeing production system has been updated and improved over the years to reach a high level of efficiency. A variety of assembly methods are used at the Everett plant, from the 787 pulsed line to the 777 moving line. During assembly, main sections are joined; landing gear, interiors and engines are installed; and power is tested. After the airplane is assembled, it's towed to a paint hangar where world class artists design and apply liveries for customers across the globe. Painting typically takes four days, then the airplane is moved to docks where it is fueled so that the fuel systems can be tested.

Ready for delivery

Finally the airplane is moved to the flight line, where everything – from engines to evacuation slides – is tested. Then the airplane is flight-tested by Boeing and the customer – when the flights are satisfactory and all systems are working smoothly, the airplane is ready for delivery.

Producing a 747-8, the largest commercial airplane Boeing makes today, involves assembling nearly 6 million parts. In 1966, Pan American World Airways announced a $525 million order for 25 Boeing 747s, effectively launching the program. The first 747-100 rolled out of the factory in 1968, and the first delivery was to Pam Am in December 1969. The fuselage of the original "Queen of the Skies" was 225 feet (68.6 meters) long and the tail was as tall as a six-story building.

747-8 EVERETT FACTORY LINE

The 747-8 is made up of approximately **6 million parts** that come together to create the world's most recognizable airplane and the most efficient airplane in its class.

747-8
FREIGHTER

A new 747-8 Freighter comes together for the first time during the final body join phase of production.

42 billion

The 747 fleet has logged more than 42 billion nautical miles (77.8 billion kilometers), equivalent to 101,500 trips from the Earth to the moon and back.

747-8

AN ALL-NEW AIRPLANE. 70 PERCENT OF THE STRUCTURAL WEIGHT OF THE 747-8 IS NEW, CONSISTING OF ADVANCED ALUMINUM ALLOYS AND COMPOSITE MATERIALS.

30%

The 747-8 is 30 percent quieter than the 747-400 due to the noise-reducing dual chevrons on the GEnx-2B engines.

The 747-8 has an all-new wing with raked wingtips – an innovative new design element that is similar to the 787 design.

Unlike other airplanes produced in the Everett factory, the 767 is assembled in one bay with the exception of the wings. The success of this one-bay, lean manufacturing line helped Boeing win the U.S. Air Force contract to build the next-generation aerial refueling tanker. Once the airplane is completed, it is rolled out of the north end of the factory on its way to the paint hangar. Production of the 767 began in 1978 with a $1.2 billion order from United Airlines. In 1981, the first 767 rolled out of the factory, ushering in the age of frequent, direct, point-to-point connections for passengers flying across the Atlantic.

767 EVERETT FACTORY LINE

The 767 was the **first widebody commercial jet** operated by a two-person crew, which became an industry standard for all commercial airplanes.

1,200

The 767-300ER holds 23,980 gallons (90,770 liters) of fuel – enough to fill 1,200 minivans. It takes only 28 minutes to fuel the airplane.

The 767 is the first widebody jet to be stretched twice. The 767-300 is 21 feet (6.43 meters) longer than the original 767-200; the 767-400ER is 21 feet (6.43 meters) longer than the 767-300.

767

COMPETITIVE SUCCESS. THE 767'S LOW OPERATING COST PER TRIP COMBINED WITH IMPECCABLE RELIABILITY AND INCREASED RANGE CAPABILITY MAKE IT A FAVORITE AMONG CARGO CARRIERS SUCH AS UPS, FEDEX AND DHL.

The tanker, known in the factory as the 767-2C, is built on the same line in the Everett factory as the rest of the 767 family.

The KC-46 delivers more fuel and carries more cargo, more passengers and more aeromedical patients than the KC-135 it is replacing.

The 777 is assembled on a moving production line in the Everett facility. Once the wings and body sections come together, the airplane moves through the process to final body join and final assembly. Since its entry into service, airlines of the world continue to marvel at the 777 performance. The airplane has both the greatest payload and longest range of any airplane in the 300- to 400-seat category. And it also flies at lower costs to the airlines. Its structural efficiency makes it the most cost-effective large twin-engine airplane in the world today.

777
EVERETT FACTORY LINE

The 777 featured some of the **first large-scale applications of composites** – the vertical fin and horizontal stabilizers are made of composite materials.

The 777 is the most successful twin-engine, long-haul airplane.

1.8 inches
(4.6 centimeters)

The 777's U-shaped production line moves at a rate of about 1.8 inches (4.6 centimeters) per minute.

777

Each 777 has approximately 3 million parts.

More than 200 million people around the globe fly the 777 each year.

The 787 Dreamliner is assembled using a unique technique called a pulsed line. During assembly, the airplane advances through four production positions – but not continuously – moving from the first position all the way to the fourth and final position in the factory. The final position is where power is applied to the airplane and functional testing occurs. From there the Dreamliner goes to the paint hangar – and final delivery. The 787-8 Dreamliner lifted off from Paine Field in Everett on its successful first flight in December 2009; the first delivery was made to Japan's ANA Sept. 25, 2011.

787 EVERETT FACTORY LINE

The 787 Dreamliner uses **20 percent less fuel** on comparable missions than other airplanes in its class. This means 20 percent fewer emissions.

70 miles
(113 kilometers)

The 787 has approximately 70 miles (113 kilometers) of wiring.

Advances in engine technology are the biggest contributor to overall fuel efficiency improvements on the 787 Dreamliner – new engines from General Electric and Rolls-Royce represent nearly a two-generation jump in technology.

787

MORE REVENUE. WITH THE 787, AIRLINES REALIZE MORE CARGO REVENUE CAPACITY — A 20 TO 45 PERCENT ADVANTAGE OVER TODAY'S SIMILARLY SIZED AIRPLANES.

The 787 is a better choice for the environment – it produces fewer emissions than airplanes of a similar size and is quieter for people on the ground.

From larger windows that create a bright interior; to the smoother, quiet ride; to soft LED lighting – thoughtfully balanced for work or rest – this airplane is made for passenger comfort.

SO BIG!

The Everett factory is so big that when it was first built it created its own weather, with clouds forming near the ceiling. When an air-circulation system was installed, the clouds cleared.

The Everett site is run just like a small city, with its own fire department, security force, fully staffed medical clinic, electrical substations and water treatment plant – even its own cafeterias and coffee shops.

Each of the hangar doors is more than half the size of a U.S. football field. The smaller doors are 81 feet (25 meters) by 300 feet (91 meters); the two larger doors are 81 feet (25 meters) by 350 feet (107 meters).

Thirty-four overhead cranes move along a 37-mile (60-kilometer) network of ceiling tracks throughout the 4.3-million square foot (399,483-square meter) factory to lift and transport up to 160,000 pounds (72,575 kilograms) of airplane components and sections.

Credits: Creation of this Everett Factory history was made possible by the design, writing and photography contributions of a host of dedicated Boeing professionals. Design by Cass Weaver. Writing by Betsy Case and other contributors. Photographs provided by Kevin Brown, Leo Dejillas, Bob Ferguson, Gail Hanusa, Jennifer Reitz, Jeremiah Scott, Tim Stake, Ed Turner and Will Wantz.

ISBN 978-0-615-78412-0